MASTERPIECE

story by **Grace Tran & Len Nguyen** | *art by* **Catherine Lian and Len Nguyen**

Scholastic Inc. New York Toronto London Auckland Sydney New Delhi Hong Kong

ORIGINAL COVER

MEET THE AUTHORS

Grace Tran   Len Nguyen   Catherine Lian

DEDICATION

"Art enables us to find ourselves and lose ourselves at the same time."
— Thomas Merton

To the Haterz:
For motivating me more than any member of the fam did – CL

To all the Stoller Summa Teachers:
You helped us more than you know – GT

To Catherine and Grace:
For doing everything that I didn't – LN

"The arts are not a way to make a living.
They are a very human way of making life more bearable. Practicing an art, no matter how well
or badly, is a way to make your soul grow, for heaven's sake.
Sing in the shower. Dance to the radio. Tell stories. Write a poem to a friend, even a lousy poem.
Do it as well as you possibly can. You will get an enormous reward.

You will have created something."
— Kurt Vonnegut

ART MUSEUM

Starry Night was a painting made by Vincent Van Gogh. In 1889, Van Gogh placed himself in a mental asylum. *Starry Night* was the view that he saw from his room just before sunrise. The painting can now be seen at the Museum of Modern Art (MOMA) in New York City.

Bridge over a Pond of Water Lilies was one of 250 other paintings by Claude Monet, a French Impressionist. Impressionism is a style of art that focuses on everyday life instead of royalty or famous people.

Edgar Degas was famous for his paintings of ballerinas.
He was fascinated by their graceful movements
and elegance. Many of his paintings showed
a typical day for the ballerinas at their studio.

Degas, a French Impressionist, painted *Ballet Rehearsal* in 1873.

The Great Wave off Kanagawa was a wood-block print by Katsushika Hokusai. Wood-block printing is a way to print onto materials such as fabric and paper.

The Great Wave was part of a series of other paintings called *Thirty-Six Views of Mount Fuji*. The painting was made during the Edo Period of Japan, which was between 1603-1867. Edo is now known as Tokyo, the capital of Japan.

Francis Picabia's *Machine Turn Quickly* was finished in 1917 and was a form of abstract art.

It was made as a part of the Dada movement which began in Switzerland in 1916. The group was formed as a response to World War I as an embrace of disorganization and chaos.

Piet Mondrian's *Comp. 10* was one of his abstract paintings featuring lines, geometric shapes, and solid colors.

Mondrian's *Gray Tree* was one of his first attempts at Cubism. Cubism is a style of painting that uses geometric shapes to depict something. Cubism paintings are not meant to be realistic.

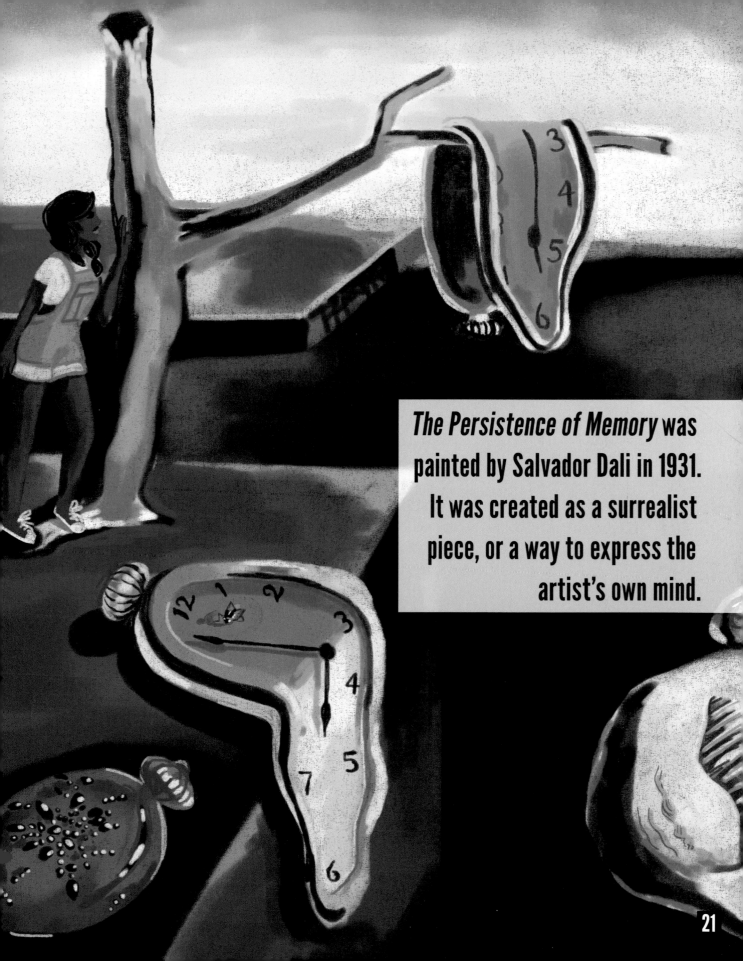

The Persistence of Memory was painted by Salvador Dali in 1931. It was created as a surrealist piece, or a way to express the artist's own mind.

Dali said himself that the painting was actually his idea of pieces of cheese melting in the sun. Today, it can be seen at the Museum of Modern Art.

Impression, Sunrise was another painting by Claude Monet. Though people later said that it was just abstract art (or art with no subject that can be understood in many different ways), the painting itself gave rise to the Impressionist movement.

Frantisek Kupka painted *Amorpha: Fugue in Two Colors* in 1912. This painting is a popular example of abstract art. This piece of art began as a girl holding a ball in her hand and gradually changed into the ribbons of color that cross the page.

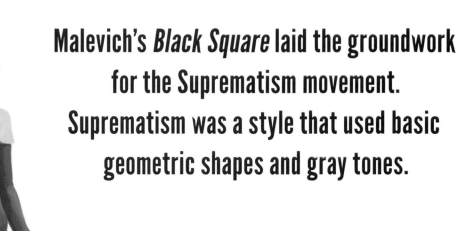

Malevich's *Black Square* laid the groundwork for the Suprematism movement. Suprematism was a style that used basic geometric shapes and gray tones.

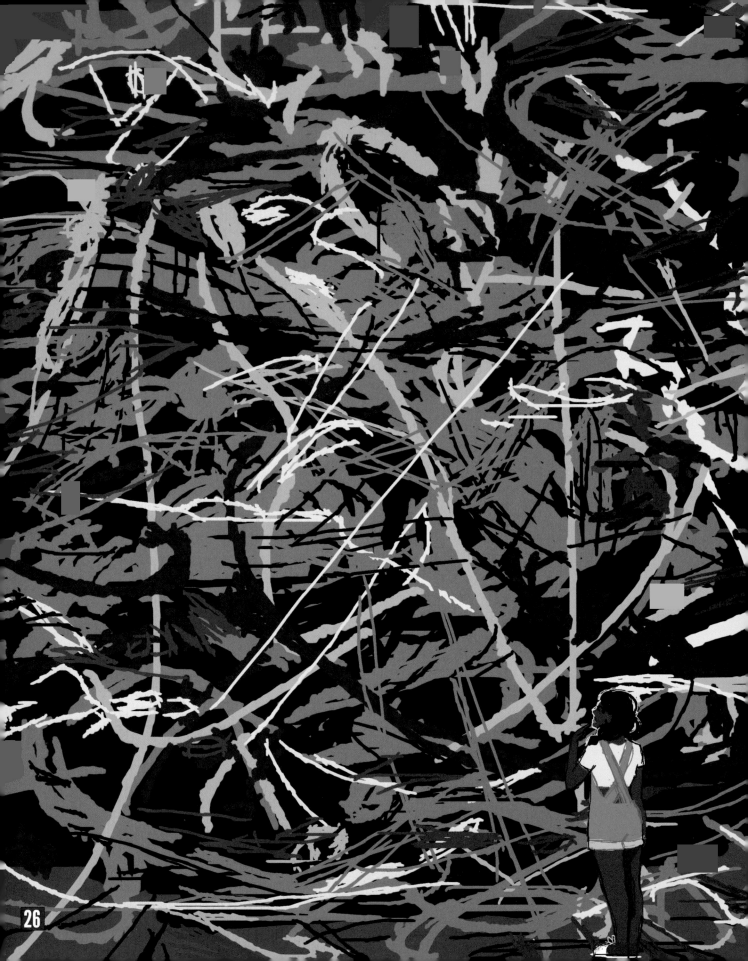

Jackson Pollock was famous for splashing paint onto canvas, a style that was later named action painting. The colors in *No. 5, 1948* created different textures and many people came to understand it differently. It was sold in 2006 for over $100 million.

Andy Warhol was a leading figure in the Pop Art movement. That means he made art based on popular culture.

Warhol was famous for his *Campbell's Soup*, which showed 32 cans of the soup lined up in a 4 by 8 rectangle. He also painted many colorful celebrities such as Marilyn Monroe and popular household items such as bottles of Coca-Cola.

Kids Are Authors®
Books written by children for children

The Kids Are Authors® Competition was established in 1986 to encourage children to read and to become involved in the creative process of writing. Since then, thousands of children have written and illustrated books as participants in the Kids Are Authors® Competition. The winning books in the annual competition are published by Scholastic Inc. and are distributed by Scholastic Book Fairs throughout the United States.

For more information:
Kids Are Authors® 1080 Greenwood Blvd., Lake Mary, FL 32746
Or visit our website at: www.scholastic.com/kidsareauthors

Cover design by Bill Henderson
Printed and bound in the U.S.A.
First Printing, June 2015